12/3/21

Kensi—

to motherhood!
thank you for your love
and support. Cent wait for
the years ahead.

With love
Katie

Mommy Didn't Say That...

Written by
Allison McGill & Charla Everhart

Illustrated by
John Paul Snead

You are the Shit!

Allison McGill

Printed in the United States of America

First Printing, 2020

ISBN 978-1-7340479-0-5 (sc)
ISBN 978-1-7340479-1-2 (hc)
ISBN 978-1-7340479-2-9 (e)

Lola & Pear
www.LolaAndPear.com

To Jack and Gavin,

Thank you for not having "That's what she said"
be your first sentence.

- Allison

To Eloise,
my kind, brave, funny, smart, and creative girl.

Please avoid cursing in front of your great-
grandparents...

But if you do, tell them you learned it from your dad.

Love, Mom

- Charla

Mommy didn't say that...

She said,
"OH SHEET!"

She forgot to fold the sheets and just realized it.

Mommy didn't use
THAT finger...

No, she was telling the other driver they were number one.

And they are! They are number one on my...

She said, "SHIP LIST."

They are number one
on my ship list.

They like ships.
I am sure of it.

Daddy didn't say THAT...

He was talking about truckers and their mothers.

It's important for truckers to call their mothers at least once a week.

No, definitely not! She said,
"That was a beachy thing to do."

Daddy didn't say that...

He said, "What the DUCK?!"

He was surprised to see a duck right there. Oh, you didn't see it? Maybe next time.

Mommy didn't say

...into bed, because if he is driving like that he must need a nap.

Mommy and Daddy
DID SAY THAT...

They said that they love you so very much, and they are trying hard to be the best for you, but sometimes they lose their cool and make mistakes.

Lola & Pear gives 20% of the profit from each book to a chosen charity.

The charity for *Mommy Didn't Say That...* is:

I (Allison McGill) suffered from postpartum anxiety, OCD, and depression after the birth of my first biological son. If you search for "Allison McGill and Postpartum," you can read all about my story.

If you think you are experiencing postpartum mental health issues, please

     call 1-800-944-4773
     text 503-894-9453
     or visit postpartum.net

We are honored to partner with them.

- The Team at Lola & Pear Publishing

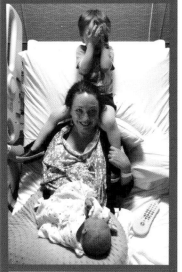

Allison McGill likes to use the bathroom without kids trying to sit on her lap, bourbon, and screaming something about hearing herself think. Those screams are often heard in Washington, DC, where she lives with her four kids, husband, and two dogs.

Charla Everhart lives in Los Angeles with her daughter, Eloise. She has rescued two birds, fallen in a manhole, and convinced Eloise to eat at least one healthy food every day since her birth.

John Paul Snead likes to hand kids back to their parents.